Marley Poppins

The Kitty Tutor

By Sommer Estrada

Dedicated to my Bengal cats: Marley, Ember, and Winny.

With love, Sommer

There once was a cat named Ember, who gave birth to a kitten in November.

The kitten was very skinny, so Ember named her Winny.

As Winny grew, Mama Ember knew there was still lots to do.

Ember taught Winny to think outside the box,
but Winny was too witty for Mama's little kitty.

So, after many, many thoughts, Winny pooped outside of the box.

Mama Ember was upset and didn't know what to do.

She would look in the box and there still was no poo.

Time went on, December was here, not pooping in the box was Mama's biggest fear.

Ember hoped, pleaded, and prayed, "Send me
Somebody to save the day."

There was a knock at the door, Ember fell to the floor. Her prayers had been answered, so fear was no more.

Marley said, "I came to help, my duties are clear, inside the box, is the goal for next year...

Let us get started, let the lessons begin!"
But January, February, and March
proved unsuccessful again.

Winny was very stubborn. Marley grew with concern. He asked himself, "Will this kitten ever learn?"

So, "Hide and Seek" came to Marley, while he cleared his mind. That is what all cats do...

Winter was behind them, and springtime was here. In April, May, and June, it became perfectly clear.

Marley must be stern, so Winny can learn. "Hide your rocks in the box!" Marley said with concern.

So, Summertime months, July, August, through September, rewarded them all... A Time to Remember.

Marley reaped the harvest of all his hard work.

Ember cried tears of joy. "In The Box" finally worked!

A full year had past, the learning had been fun.

He had helped another good family, Marley had to depart.

But forever and ever,
Marley will be in their hearts.
The End.

A Winny issue.

Based on a true story about my Bengal cat family. Winny still has not learned to use the litter box for poo poo #2. Mama Ember did her best raising her, but Winny is still overthinking the litter box in the poo department.

Made in the USA
Monee, IL
22 November 2020